For Dan,
who likes snow a lot.
Nicola

Pour ma maman,
qui aime beaucoup
les Inuits!
Sébastien

First published in 2018
by Scholastic Children's Books
Euston House, 24 Eversholt Street
London NW1 1DB
a division of Scholastic Ltd
www.scholastic.co.uk
London ~ New York ~ Toronto ~ Sydney ~ Auckland
Mexico City ~ New Delhi ~ Hong Kong

Text copyright © 2018 Nicola Davies
Illustrations copyright © 2018 Sebastien Braun

PB ISBN 978 1407 15742 9

BRAVE AND THE FOX

Nicola Davies • Sebastien Braun

SCHOLASTIC

The long, dark winter was over at last!
The sun shone down on the village under Blue Mountain,
where Brave was getting ready for her very first hunting trip.

Granny gave Brave a bag to carry with her, always. Inside there
was a cup to hold melted snow, a lamp for light and warmth,
a flint and dry bark to make the flame, and a fish hook.

"This is all a brave girl really needs."
Granny said, "Fire, water and food,
always keep them close!"

Granny and Brave loaded the dog sled and
raced away from the village.
The air still had icy teeth, but they were cosy
inside their fur-lined parkas and mittens.

The dogs' feet pattered and the sled runners
shush-shushed, out over the frozen sea.

When the sun began to dip behind Blue Mountain
they knew it was time to make a camp.
Granny cut blocks of snow to make an igloo.
"Now," she said, "it's your turn!"

It took Brave much longer to make her snow house.
Granny helped to cut the last block out of ice.
"So you can have a window, and see the sky!" she said.

Soon Granny was asleep and the dogs had closed their eyes, but Brave lay awake for a long time watching the aurora dance around the stars.

oooooooo-aaaaahhhh

weeeeeeee-oooooooo

grmmp-grmmp-grmmp

She dreamed of the bowhead whales swimming in the water underneath her igloo.
In her dream she sang with them…

Brave was so deep in her whale dreams…

that she didn't hear the ice split apart…

and send her drifting.

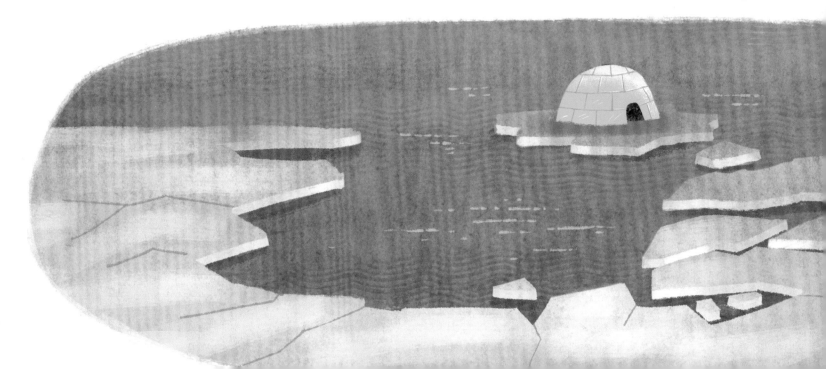

In the morning, when Brave woke, there was no sound of hungry dogs or Granny calling out her name. All she could hear was the chit-chit-chit of the ice floes knocking together.

She went outside and saw that Blue Mountain
was just a baby's tooth on the horizon.
All she could see was ice and ocean…

and a small, white fox.

But there was no time to wonder how the fox
had got there, because the igloo island had
started to break. There was only time to…

Jump!

The cracked ice looked like a maze,
but the little fox led the way and Brave followed.

From floe

to floe,

faster

and faster

and faster

until, with one last

Leap...

they landed on solid ice,

sliding and tumbling, rolling over and over

and skidding into a snowdrift that felt warm and furry…

It was a
polar bear!

The bear woke at once and snapped its jaws.
It missed the fox. It missed Brave.

But it bit her bag and held on tight.
If she pulled back, the bear might eat her. If she let go, she would lose the
fire, water and food – and without them she wouldn't make it home.

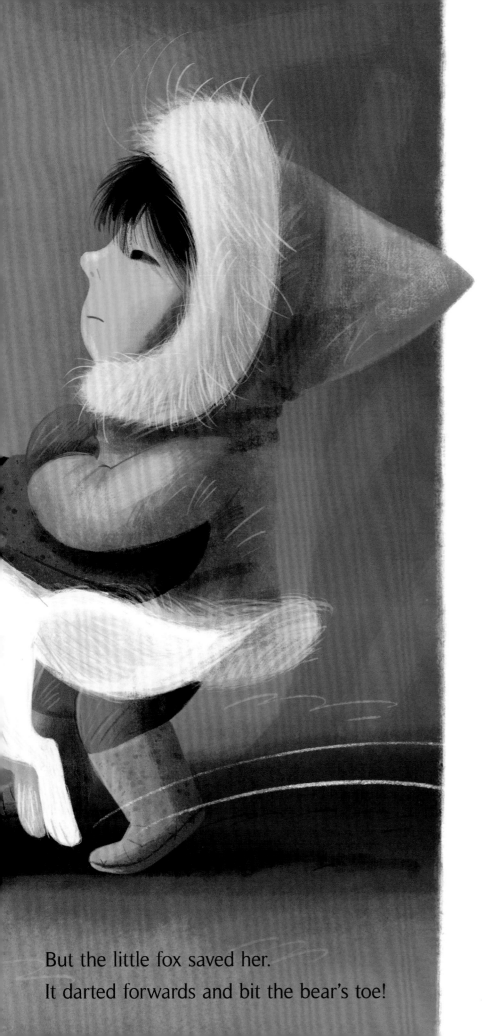

As the bear's mouth opened in a roar of pain, Brave pulled her bag free. Then she slipped her hand out of a mitten, and threw it down.

By the time the bear had sniffed it, chewed it, and spat the mitten out, Brave had got away.

But the little fox saved her.
It darted forwards and bit the bear's toe!

She looked around to thank the fox, but it was nowhere to be seen.
Alone again, she trudged on towards her home, so very far away.

The sun began to sink. Clouds came, and a blizzard shrieked down from the sky.
Brave knew she must make a shelter from the storm, but cold bit her bare hand.

Snow swirled and filled her eyes so she couldn't see.
Brave felt lost and frightened. She sank down in the snow and closed her eyes.

Something brushed against her face,
softer than a snowflake.
The fox!

It dropped her missing
mitten in her lap.

It was very chewed, but good enough to keep
the cold from nibbling at her fingers.

Brave jumped up and began to
scoop the snow to make a dip,
a hole, a cave – a haven from
the snowstorm's wind and cold.

Inside, she struck the flint, and made a flame.
She melted snow in the cup
so they could drink.

Then, in the yellow light,
they curled around each other and went to sleep.

In the morning they dug out of their drift to find a world bright white and almost blinding. Brave put on her snow goggles and the fox sniffed at her to be certain she was still herself.

They borrowed a breathing hole
belonging to a seal and used the hook to catch a fish.

And on they went.
As they walked,
the Blue Mountain
grew from baby's tooth,

to walrus tusk,

to whale.

They were almost home.

But they reached a split in the ice – not just a crack,
a chasm – wide and blue, with no way to get across.

Brave felt so tired.
She thought of Granny and the village underneath the mountain.
So close but still so far away.
A song began to sing itself inside her heart…

OOOOOOOO - aaaaahhh

weeeeeeee - ooooooooooo

grunp-grunp-grunp

...and from her heart it sang into the still, cold air,
and through the ice, and down, down, down into the sea
until it reached the whales. And they sang back.

OOOOOOOO-aaaaahhhh

weeeeeeee-ooooooo

grmmp-grmmp-grmmp

One-by-one they came and side-by-side they swam, a line of wide grey backs
like living stepping stones leading Brave and her fox home.

The whole village came to greet the little girl
who had found her way alone across the frozen sea.

Her Granny hugged her, proud as proud.

"Fire, water, food!" her Granny said, "You kept them close."
Brave smiled. "Fire, water, food,
and a friend!" she said.

Why does the ice crack while Brave is asleep?

During the long winter, when it is dark most of the time, the Arctic Ocean freezes. The ice is so thick that it is safe to travel on, even in early Spring. But, some years, the ice starts to thaw and break up earlier than expected. This is why Brave found herself floating on an ice island, or floe.

What is climate change?

The climate of our world is changing, so that weather and seasons may not be what we expect! This is called climate change or global warming.

In the Arctic, Springs arrive earlier and Summers are warmer each year. Every year the sea ice melts sooner in the Spring and freezes later in the Autumn. This makes a big difference to Arctic people and animals, who depend on sea ice for safe travel and for places to hunt seals and catch fish.

What causes climate change?

Climate change is caused by changes in the earth's atmosphere – the air that's all around us. Humans have burned so much coal, oil and gas to heat houses, drive cars and power factories, that the air has changed. There is more of a gas called carbon dioxide in the air now, and that makes the air like a blanket, keeping our planet a bit too warm.

How does climate change affect our world?

Being 'a bit too warm' doesn't sound like much, but it can mean big changes. It makes big storms and hurricanes happen more often. It causes long droughts in some places and floods in others. It makes the weather patterns unpredictable, so it can be hard for farmers to know when to plant their crops for a good harvest. It changes habitats so that animals can find it hard to survive.

What can we do to help stop global warming?

We need to stop putting more and more carbon dioxide into the air.

Making electricity from the sun, wind and sea really helps.

But you can help too in all kinds of small ways!

*Ride your bike to school
instead of riding in a car or bus.*

*Put on an extra sweater instead of
turning up the heat in your bedroom.*

*Grow vegetables in your school or home garden so you don't have to
buy veg that has been carried to the shops in aeroplanes and trucks.*

And tell all the grown ups you know to do the same!

If we all work together, we can get around this big problem.